Foreward by Louise Goodman

I've just finished recceing for the 1999 Network Q Rally of Great Britain as I write this. Thankfully Jim wasn't with me, because we could have filled another edition of "The Pits" with my mishaps and cock-ups. But that's Jim's talent. He has a wonderfully wicked eye and finds humour around every corner of every race track and special stage. That's a rare and precious commodity in a sport which, on occasion has been known to take itself far too seriously! So thanks for all the laughter you've given us over the years Jim - and keep those pencils sharpened!

Louise Goodman
Somewhere in a forest, Wales

The Pits 7 is an Autosport Special Project published by Haymarket Autosport Publications, 38-42 Hampton Road, Teddington, Middx, TW11 0JE England. Tel: 44 (0)208 267 5000 Fax 44 (0)208 267 5079. Printed in England by B R Hubbard, Dronfield, Sheffield. Origination by Primary Colours (Although in this particular case it's more like Primary Black and White), Chiswick, London.

We celebrate the year of the so called also ran. Eddie Irvine, Matt Neal, David Higgins and some foreign chappie called Bugalski. All of them stirred up the pot and brought a little excitement into what is becoming a predictable sport. The money won the British Rally Championship and then, marketing exercise over, split. Once again another foreign driver most British fans had never heard of won the British Touring Car Championship. Tommi Makinen won the World Rally Championship for the <u>fourth</u> consecutive year and fellow Finn Mika Hakkinen won the Formula One World Championship...again.
Ferrari continued to shoot themselves in the foot, Nigel Roebuck still thinks Jean Alesi is a great driver and the Scottish football team still play like a bunch of...oops we seem to have strayed from the points, which I believe is what Craig Pollock said to Jacques Villeneuve.
My thanks to Louise for writing the foreword - her parents think I'm very brave. A sad farewell to John Cleland who has more character in his little finger than I have in mine. And last but not least spare a thought for poor Eddie Irvine... sunning himself on some remote Pacific island thinking about his year and his yacht and his millions and his jet and his Ferraris and his women. Yes spare a thought for poor Eddie. I certainly will. Enjoy the book.

Jim Bamber

www.jimbamber.co.uk

4

To understand this you have to know your history. November 5 1956.

The "Pursuit of excellence" begins

— Silverstone's Show stoppers!

I'm not supposed to tell you this, but the sexy one on the right is Katie from Silverstone

For Sale: Toyota bookends, matching pair, low mileage - apply Carlos Sainz and
Luis 'Basil' Moya, c/o Faulty Toyotas, Cologne.

Wow! The new Ford Focus arrived in Monte Carlo with a bang. A wake up call for all concerned

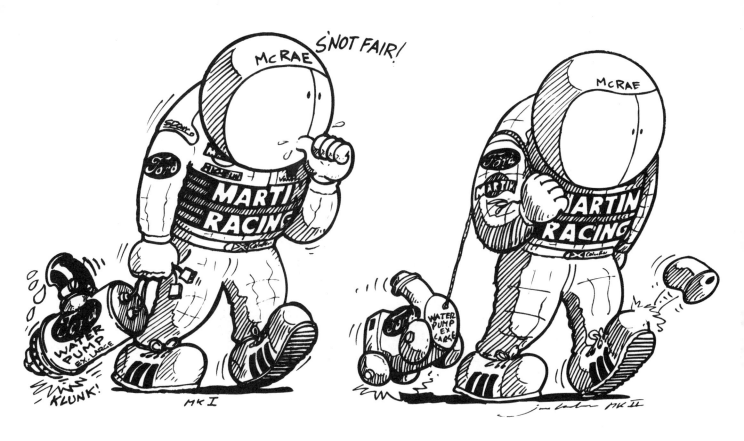

To show everybody that Ford still had a sense of humour, following the waterpump fiasco, Ford boss Martin Whitaker asked me to draw a cartoon that was to be stuck on the side of the WRC Focus for the Swedish Rally. The one on the left was rejected. Couldn't have the six million dollar man sulking <u>too</u> much could we?

How wrong can I have been? At the start of the year we all thought that Frentzen was the plonker in the Jordan team but very soon the positions would be reversed.

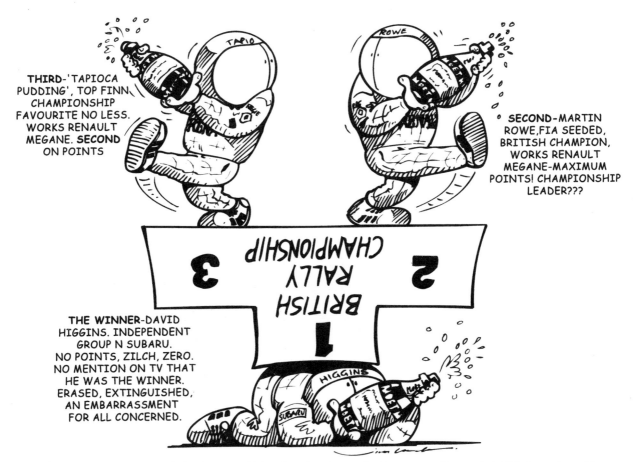

THIRD-'TAPIOCA PUDDING', TOP FINN CHAMPIONSHIP FAVOURITE NO LESS. WORKS RENAULT MEGANE. **SECOND** ON POINTS

SECOND-MARTIN ROWE, FIA SEEDED, BRITISH CHAMPION, WORKS RENAULT MEGANE-MAXIMUM POINTS! CHAMPIONSHIP LEADER???

THE WINNER-DAVID HIGGINS. INDEPENDENT GROUP N SUBARU. NO POINTS, ZILCH, ZERO. NO MENTION ON TV THAT HE WAS THE WINNER. ERASED, EXTINGUISHED, AN EMBARRASSMENT FOR ALL CONCERNED.

"The first shall be last and the last shall be first" - Jesus that's a great line, wish I'd thought of it.
It's actually the new motto for the British Rally Championship!

19

David and Michael sparring with their handbags during testing at Barcelona. Autosport used the milder 'blancmange' flavoured version that week.

21

This was drawn in March! Nuf said.

The expected revolution in digital viewing was slow in coming. Couldn't possibly have anything to do with the product could it?

I was wrong with this. I thought Craig was part of the American abstract school of painting when in fact he was a student of Pointillism...or the lack of it.

Irvine wins his first Grand Prix. Great stuff.

No this isn't July already, Schumacher was complaining of a sore ankle early in the year.

Makinen was excluded from the Safari Rally when he was spotted having his wheel changed by a wandering tribe of Kwik Fit Fitters.

Formula 3 rookie team Manor Motorsport became the first team in eight years to win its maiden race in the British Championship.

The first shunt of the year at Silverstone was during the National Saloon Cup sponsored by the circuit's own Insurance Services.

The British Touring Car Championship hero of the year, Matt Neal!

The McLaren boys were back in Brazil.

There was talk that Manchester United was to be sold so Nicola Foulston jumps up and says she wants to buy ...Silverstone?

This refers to a statement made by a certain Frenchman who said that our Colin "drives like a girl".

Citroen annoyed the big boys with their big toys when they won not one but two World Championship rallies.

47

This was the week 'Holy Hoddle' was sacked as England's manager after remarks he made about the disabled. Autosport refused to run this as they thought it would offend...wait for it, the Marshals!

I enjoyed doing this.

The BRDC member who said he likes Brands Hatch!

A boring Spanish Grand Prix came right after the most exciting
European Football Cup Final seen in years.

It <u>was</u> dull at first but Schumacher would soon change all that.

'Handbagitus' was catching on in rallying when Ricky Burnup and co-driver Robert Reid went all sulky after Juha Kankkunen 'poached' Burns' victory in Argentina.

In the first Kosovo Grand Prix the Russians showed they had the fastest tanks arriving 24 hours before NATO.

Once is happenstance, twice is coincidence, but three times is bloody stupid!

64

Before the British Grand Prix Damon was at sixes and sevens, and even last on one occasion.

Oops! This was done the week before the British Grand Prix.

This was drawn as a small thank you to the Grand Prix doctors for inviting me to a bit of a do just before the British Grand Prix. The other invited guests turned out to be Nick Mason, Stirling Moss and Lord Hesketh! For some reason the words, "trumpet" and "blowing your own" seem to pop into my head!

69

This is where the year really started.

In Austria David put the boot into Hakkinen, and about time too.

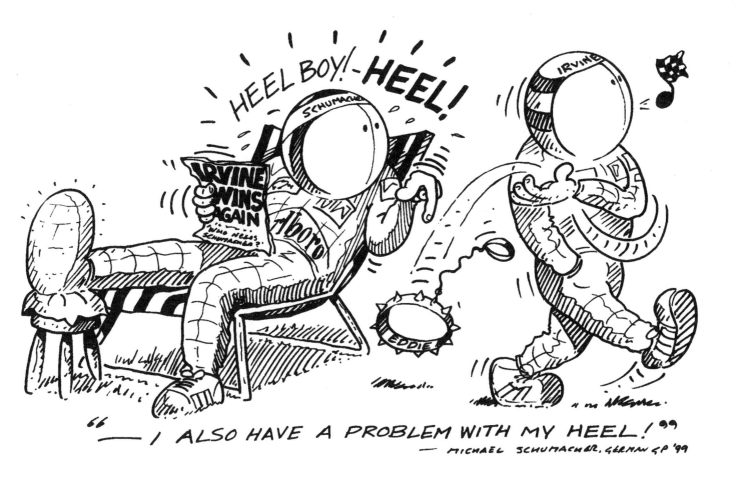

To Schumacher's horror Irvine kept on winning.

Schumacher was desperate to get back... or was he?

PHUT!

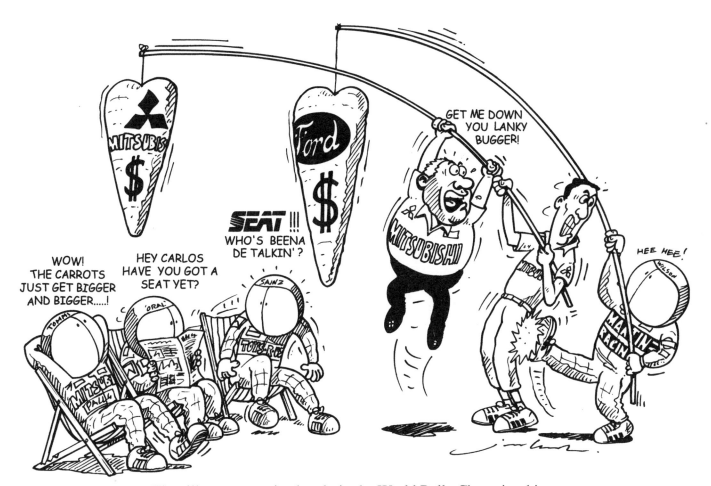

The silly season arrived early in the World Rally Championship.

Schumacher did the five second cockpit test easily but still stayed home.

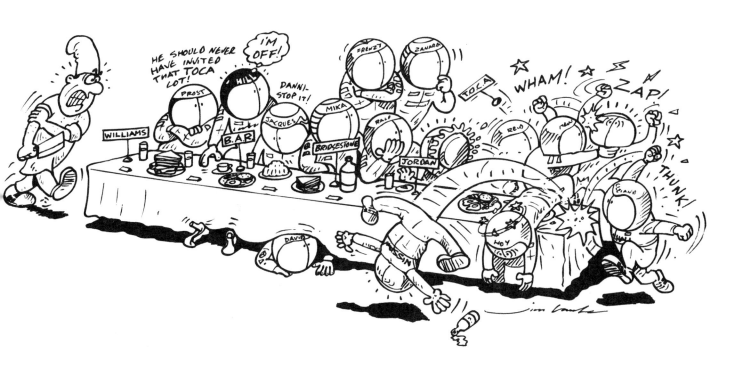

The fat controller otherwise known as Paul Edwards, the F1 chef, reached his half century and had a big party, and I mean a BIG party.

This was for the lads of the Group B car club. Their guest for the day at Castle Combe was French rally star Jean Ragnotti

Hakkinen wasn't the only McLaren driver who enjoyed huge support in Hungary.

The "Pursuit of excellence" continued at Spa.

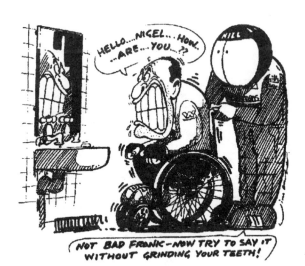

In the end he sold it to some bankers.

91

I was wrong with this one too. It wasn't Mika they were sticking pins into, it was Eddie!

After Hakkinen's tears at Monza it was Muller's turn after gifting victory to Panoz at Road Atlanta.

A birthday present for a doctor friend who drives a bubble car. Well somebodys got to.

This was for the mechanics at Big Mal's place in Cumbria.

I ask you, would they have done this if it had been Michael driving? I think not.

This was done for Jason Plato as a thank you to Frank Williams for giving him the Renault drive. Seems that when Jason went begging for the seat he just wouldn't leave Frank alone until he said yes.

103

When Toyota decided to move into F1 Carlos went looking for the second seat at Ford. Dream team or stuff of nightmares? Can't wait.

No more John Cleland in the BTCC. The world just won't be the same.

He was back and he was meaner than ever.

Francois Delecour was given a two minute penalty for infringing the most stupid rule in the history of Motorsport. He rode a bike on a public road two days before the San Remo rally proper began.

My lips are sealed.

OKAY– I WIN THE BRITISH GRAND PRIX, AND YOU CAN WIN THE GERMAN!
HILL
SCHUMACHER
FRENCH GRAND PRIX
LET'S HEAR IT FOR AUSTRIA!
BERGER

Irvine was off to Paris for a weekend with...

...Max?

...and they all lived happily ever after.

Goodbye Damon-thanks for all the laughter..and the tears.

History teaches us that nothing changes. It took the authorities 20 years to decide who had won the first RAC Rally held in 1932. It was the chauffeur.

In the old days the RAC Rally was a lot meatier...

♪ THERE'LL BE A WELCOME IN THE HILLSIDES...... ♪

...than the homogenised rubbish we get today.

128